Pol and Pax on the third moon

Hannie Truijens

Illustrated by
John Harrold and Steve Smallman

Chapter 1 Take-off page 3

Chapter 2 The Wham-Bams page 12

Chapter 3 The Updowns page 20

Chapter 4 The ring page 26

Nelson

Thomas Nelson and Sons Ltd
Nelson House   Mayfield Road
Walton-on-Thames   Surrey
KT12 5PL   UK

51 York Place
Edinburgh
EH1 3JD   UK

Nelson Blackie
Wester Cleddens Road
Bishopbriggs
Glasgow
G64 2NZ   UK

Thomas Nelson (Hong Kong) Ltd
Toppan Building 10/F
22A Westlands Road
Quarry Bay   Hong Kong

Thomas Nelson Australia
102 Dodds Street
South Melbourne
Victoria 3205   Australia

Nelson Canada
1120 Birchmount Road
Scarborough   Ontario
M1K 5G4   Canada

Text © J.C.M. Truijens 1989
Illustrations © Thomas Nelson & Sons Ltd 1992
Illustrated by John Harrold and Steve Smallman

First published by Macmillan Education Ltd 1989

This edition published by Thomas Nelson and Sons Ltd 1992

ISBN 0-17-422495-8
NPN 9 8 7 6 5 4

Printed in China

Chapter 1: Take-off

There is a planet, far away, which has
three moons and a ring around it.
The people who live on the planet are
shorter, rounder and much more clever than us.
They are clever because they eat
brain food when they are young.
They never have to learn anything, so
they never have to go to school.
  Pol and Pax live on the planet of
the three moons.
They play all day long, but always playing
can be just as dull as always having to work.

Pol and Pax have special inventing
tools. They can make anything they like
with their inventing tools.
A whole week long they teased each other
with their inventions.

Their parents said, "Why don't you two
go and find something to do? You're getting
in our way and making too much noise."

Pol and Pax looked at each other.
Even they were tired of teasing.

"Let's invent a rocket," said Pol.

"And go to the third moon," said Pax.

Pol and Pax went to the workshop and invented a rocket. It had to be very light, so that it wouldn't use too much fuel.
It had to be very fast, so that it would get to the third moon, and it had to be very strong, so that it wouldn't break when it landed.

Pol and Pax had to invent for three days and during those three days they didn't tease each other at all.

Pol and Pax loaded the rocket with lots
of brain food. They also put all their
inventing tools on board.

"It's better to be well prepared," said Pax.

"You never know what we may have to invent,"
said Pol.

Their parents came to see them off.

"Have a good time," they said, "but look out
for the Wham-Bams. They can be very nasty
when they are in a bad mood."

"Five, four, three, two, one, zero,"
said Pol.

"We have lift-off," shouted Pax, and
away they went.
Soon the rocket port was only a small dot.
Pol and Pax were heading for the ring
around their planet.

The ring around the planet of the three
moons shines very brightly, as if it is
polished every day.

"Who polishes the ring?" asked Pol.

"I don't know," said Pax, "but I'm glad
I don't have to do it."

Pol looked at the fuel meter. "Hooray,
our rocket is light enough," he said.
"We have enough fuel to get to the
third moon and back.
Which is the third moon, Pax?"

"It's the biggest one," said Pax. "Turn
the left handle and then press the red
button. The rocket will do the rest.
Let's have something to eat."

In space things float around and the
brain food kept floating out of reach.
Pol and Pax invented super-sharp forks to
catch the brain food.

After they had eaten Pol and Pax went to sleep. When they woke up the third moon was already very close.

They looked at the big hills and craters.

"I think we should land on that sand patch," said Pax. "Put the motor into reverse and throw out the parachute."

Pol threw out the parachute and put the motor into reverse. The rocket slowed down. It floated down slowly and landed on the sand patch. But . . . it wasn't sand.

9

Pol and Pax had landed in a lake.
It looked like sand but it was water, and
it was very hot.
The rocket went to the bottom of the lake and
came up again. Pol and Pax nearly
cooked inside the rocket.
They took out their inventing tools and
soon invented a fan.

"Phew, that's better," said Pax, when
the fan was working. "How do we get out of
this lake, Pol?"

"We'll have to invent something," said Pol.

Pax invented a hot-lake paddler and Pol packed all their brain food and tools onto it. They left the rocket on the lake. The heat of the lake made the paddles go round, and Pol and Pax sat and fanned themselves.

When they got to the side of the lake there was a crowd of Wham-Bams waiting for them. They didn't look very friendly. In fact, they were all in a bad mood.

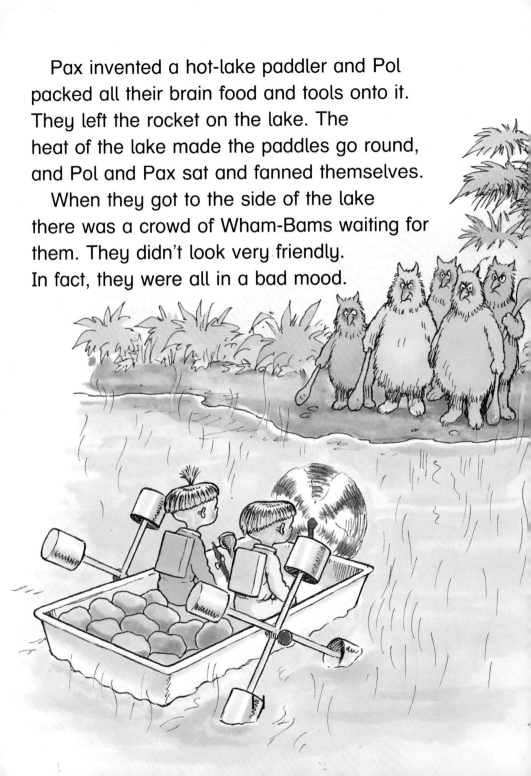

Chapter 2: The Wham-Bams

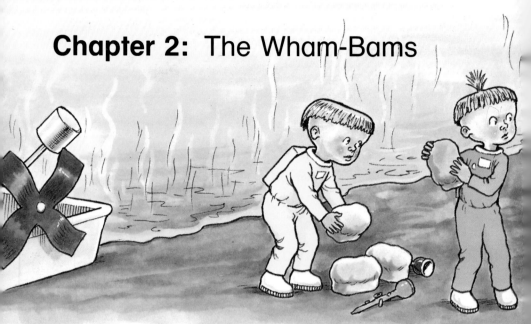

"Who are you two-who?" said the biggest
Wham-Bam. "And what are you doing here-near?"
(That's the way Wham-Bams talk.)

"We're Pol and Pax," said Pax.

"And we have come to visit the third moon,"
said Pol.

"Who said that you could-would?" said
the smallest Wham-Bam. "And what have you got
there-where?" The Wham-Bam pointed at the
box of brain food.

"That's our food," said Pol.

"And it's no good for you," said Pax.

They shouldn't have said that, of course. "Everything is good for us-bus," said the biggest Wham-Bam.

"And everything on the third moon is ours-flowers," said the smallest Wham-Bam.

"So give us that bread-head," shouted all the Wham-Bams.

Pol and Pax didn't even have time to invent a fighting machine.
The Wham-Bams were all over them, took their box of brain food, and dragged them off to the Chief Wham-Bam.

The Chief Wham-Bam was also in a
bad mood. He was hot and hungry.
He was hot because it was always hot on
the third moon, and he was hungry
because nearly everything that grew on the
third moon tasted like spinach.
He was sick and tired of spinach.

"Who do we have here-near?" he shouted.
"And what have they got-not?"

"They are strangers-dangers," said the
big Wham-Bam.

"And they have something to eat-meat,"
said the little Wham-Bam.

The Chief Wham-Bam looked at the
brain food, poked at it, sniffed it, and
then broke off a piece and ate it.
And, wonder of wonders, it didn't
taste like spinach.
He broke off another bit and
stuffed it into his mouth.
Before Pol and Pax could stop him
he had eaten half of the brain food.
    Wham-Bams are very stupid and the Chief
Wham-Bam was no better than the rest.
But with all that brain food in him . . .

The Chief Wham-Bam started thinking and thinking and thinking. And for the first time in his life he came up with a good idea.

"I have thought of a good plan-man," he said. "You two will work for me-we. You must make lots of this food and I will never have to eat spinach again-main."

Pol and Pax didn't know what to do. There were lots of nasty Wham-Bams and only two of them.

"We'd better start inventing," said Pol.

Pol and Pax invented a super-fast seed sower and sowed some brain food seed. They invented a super-cold water cooler and cooled the water of the lake. They invented a super-wide water sprinkler and watered the small brain food plants.

When the brain food plants were big enough they invented a super-strong do-it-all to reap the brain food pods, grind them into flour, mix the flour into dough and bake the dough into bread.

The Wham-Bams stood at the other end of
the do-it-all and gobbled up the brain food
as fast as they could.

Soon all the Wham-Bams had eaten so much
brain food that they were as clever as they
would ever be – which is still not very clever.

"That's enough-rough," said the Chief
Wham-bam.

"We're all very full-bull," said the
biggest Wham-Bam.

"You can stop now-how," said the
smallest Wham-Bam.

The Wham-Bams were now all in a good mood and the Chief Wham-Bam was in the best mood of all.

"We are setting you free-bee," he said to Pol and Pax.

"We will pull your rocket out of the lake-take," said the biggest Wham-Bam.

"And then you can go home-roam," said the smallest Wham-Bam.

Pol and Pax took all the brain food that was left, loaded it into the rocket and got ready to take off.

Chapter 3: The Updowns

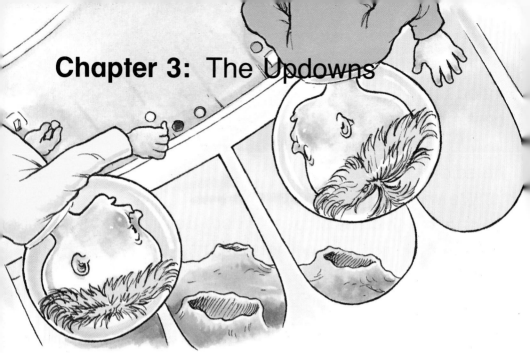

"Five, four, three, two, one, zero,"
said Pax. "We have lift-off," said Pol.
They did have lift-off, but it didn't take
them very far. The hot lake water had
got into the motor of the rocket.
It spat and spluttered and then
stopped altogether.
The rocket came down on the other
side of the third moon.

"Oh help-yelp," shouted Pol.

"Oh no-go," cried Pax. (Wham-Bam talk is
very catching.)

Pol and Pax got out of their rocket.

"We must invent a super-fast motor dryer," said Pol. They started to invent, but their invention went all wrong.

"How strange," said Pax, "a failed invention. I have never had a failed invention."

The invention was no good at all. It was upside-down and back-to-front.

"Surprising not that's," said a voice.

"Here is it way the that's," said another voice.

"Land front-to-back and down-upside is this," said a third voice.

Pol and Pax looked around them. They saw lots of upside-down and back-to-front people.

"Who are you?" asked Pol and Pax.

"Updowns are we," said the oldest Updown.

"Ground the under live we," said the youngest Updown, "Queen our meet and come."

Pol and Pax went home with the Updowns.
They were kind and not in the least like the
Wham-Bams.
They gave Pol and Pax food and drink.
The Updown Queen asked them to tell their story.
    "From come you do where?" she asked.
"Rocket your with wrong what's and?"
    Pol and Pax tried to tell their story, but
it is difficult to talk to upside-down people.
You just can't tell whether they are looking
at you or not. So they stood on their
hands and then it went much better.

23

Pol and Pax stayed with the Updowns for two weeks, and soon they could also do everything upside-down.

Every night the Updown Queen asked them to tell a different story.
All the Updowns sat around them and listened.
They always clapped their feet and said, "Story good a what."

Pol and Pax had soon run out of stories, and they were also homesick. "We would like to go home," they said to the Updown Queen.

24

"Rocket your fix and go," said the oldest Updown. "Work now will inventions your."

Pol and Pax went to their rocket and started to invent. They invented upside-down and back-to-front, and their invention came out right. Soon they were ready to take off.

"Journey good a have," said the youngest Updown. "You miss shall we."

"Goodbye and you thank," said Pol.

"Again you see to hope," said Pax.

(Updown talk is also very catching.)

Chapter 4: The ring

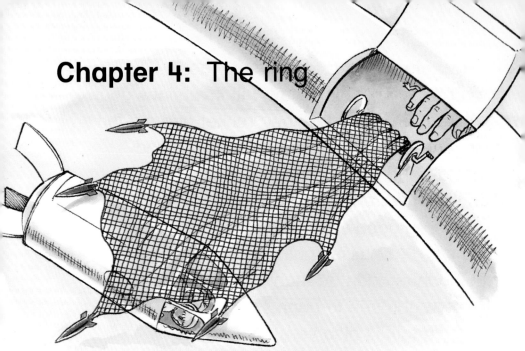

"Zero, one, two, three, four, five," said Pol.

"Lift-off have we," said Pax. And they did. They were soon travelling back to the ring around their planet.

Pol and Pax flew very close to the ring. Suddenly something went wrong with their rocket. It went slower and slower and then it stopped altogether.

"What's wrong?" shouted Pol.

"I don't know," cried Pax. (In their fright they forgot their Updown talk.)

The ring had got them. It had thrown
out a rocket trap to catch them.
A door in the ring opened up and
in went the rocket.

Pol and Pax looked at each other. They
didn't know what to do.

The door of the rocket was opened and
a long thin hand crept inside.
It grabbed Pol and pulled him out of the rocket.
Another long thin hand grabbed Pax.

27

The Hands took them to the Feet and
the Feet took them to the Body.
The Body carried them to the Neck, and
the Neck took them to the Head.
The Head said, "You must be punished."

"Why must we be punished?" asked Pol.

"What did we do wrong?" asked Pax.

"You flew too close to the ring," said
the Head. "The ring is top secret, and
nobody is allowed to fly close to it."

28

"We didn't know that," said Pol.

"Please forgive us," said Pax.

"Hard luck," said the Head. "You will still have to be punished. You will have to work for us for a hundred years. That will give the Hands some rest. Your work will be to keep the ring bright and shiny. Here is the ring polish and some cloths."

Pol and Pax started to polish. It was hard work. There was no end to the ring.

"A hundred years is a long time," said Pax.

"We'd better invent a ring polisher," said Pol.

When the Head was having a little nap they stopped polishing and started to invent. They invented a super-long ring polisher with one hundred hands. When the Head woke up it was already polishing.

The Head nodded with pleasure and the Hands clapped.

"You are free," said the Head. "We'll never have to work again," said the Hands.

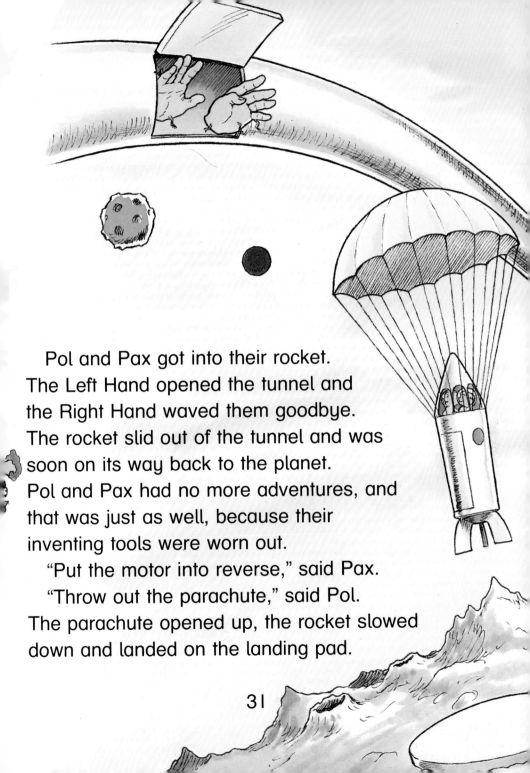

Pol and Pax got into their rocket.
The Left Hand opened the tunnel and
the Right Hand waved them goodbye.
The rocket slid out of the tunnel and was
soon on its way back to the planet.
Pol and Pax had no more adventures, and
that was just as well, because their
inventing tools were worn out.

"Put the motor into reverse," said Pax.

"Throw out the parachute," said Pol.
The parachute opened up, the rocket slowed
down and landed on the landing pad.

Pol and Pax parked their rocket and went home. Their parents were happy to see them.

"What did you see on the third moon?" they asked.

Pol and Pax told them all their adventures. They spoke Wham-Bam talk and Updown talk, and showed them how they could do things upside-down and back-to-front.

"We would like some new inventing tools for our birthday," said Pol.

"Ours are all worn out," said Pax.